**KICKS
BUTT**

By the same author
Maggie's Farm
Further Down on Maggie's Farm
Maggie's Farm - The Last Roundup*
The If... Chronicles*
If... Only Again*
Another Load of If...*
The Unrepeatable If...*
If... Bounces Back*
If... Breezes In*
The Vengeance of If...*
The Revolutionary If...*

with Brian Homer
Waiting for the Upturn*

with Roger Woddis
Funny Old World

*published by Mandarin

Steve Bell  KICKS BUTT

MANDARIN

For Heather, William, Joey, Paddy and Kit Kat

This collection first published in Great Britain in 1991
by Mandarin
Michelin House, 81 Fulham Road, London SW3 6RB

The strips first published by *The Guardian* in 1990 and 1991

Copyright © Steve Bell 1990, 1991

Designed by Brian Homer

Production by Andy Coyne

Edited by Steve Bell and Brian Homer

Linotronic playout by Typesetters, Birmingham Ltd

Printed and bound in Great Britain
by Richard Clay Ltd, Bungay, Suffolk

ISBN 0 07493 0816 8

A CIP catalogue record for this book
is available from the British Library

JUNE

5

THE STORY SO FAR:

JUNE 1990 - THE CLOSING MONTHS OF THE THATCHER ERA. **BIG TOM,** AN OVERWEIGHT, OVERSEXED WANDSWORTH CAT, IS TIRED OF A DIET OF ULTRA-SAFE, ULTRA-BLAND **©GUMMERBRAINS®™-** AND IS IN SEARCH OF FOOD THAT IS NEITHER **UNWHOLESOME** NOR **UNHINGED**.....

7

OUR VALUE SYSTEM IS ALL WRONG.....

...I MUST HAVE THAT SHIRT!

...EVERYBODY IS OUT FOR **NUMBER ONE** AND NOBODY SEEMS TO CARE ABOUT THE **PLANET**..... I MEAN; THE COWS, THE SHEEP, THE PIGS, THE FISH, THEY'VE ALL BEEN DRIVEN **MAD** BY INTENSIVE FARMING......

....IT REALLY IS A **BEAUTY!**

...WHICH MEANS I CAN NO LONGER EAT THE BASTARDS AND MAINTAIN MY **MENTAL EQUILIBRIUM**..

...I CAN'T TAKE MY EYES OFF IT!

...WHAT WE NEED IS A **GLOBAL SENSE OF SPIRITUAL REGENERATION**

...I'M GONNA HAVE TO **SEIZE IT** ' BEFORE I START FOAMING AT THE MOUTH!!

I LIKE THE **SHIRT**, BIG TOM!

JOIN THE **QUEUE**, DOLL!

GOD, BIOLOGY IS SO **DEGRADING** SOMETIMES

....I MEAN — LOOK AT US QUEUING UP TO BE **SERVICED** BY THAT **FAT GIT**....AND WHY?? WHY??

BECAUSE THE **LOUDER** THE SHIRT, THE MORE ROBUST THE GENES — —THAT'S **SCIENTIFIC FACT!**

NEXT!

8

An SDP memorial barbecue......

Nine yearsh o' my life — but they've not bin wayshted yearsh, 'ave they 'Arry ??

You what?

RRIP

SLASH

—15.6.24.26—

Sh bin goojearsh 'Arry.... Shalorra claret bin shunk, but thasshall bollocksh innit 'Arry.... Ya claret'shnorr important... Shnot himportant't'tall...

What you on about, Ned? What's not important ??

The claret'n'all that—sshooperfisshull... ...I'm talkin' 'bout the essh deeepee'sh real contribution to Brish poltics... ...I'm talkin 'bout the hairshtylesh!!

....Aaaarrrgghhh!! The cat'sh got me rug!!!

LUNGE

© Steve Bell 1990

Bald, clapped-out, pisshed, an' the party I love ish no more. What am I good for, Harry? What are any of us has-beens good for??

SPEAK FOR YOURSELF

Of course — you've still got your hair, haven't you, Death?....And you haven't lost any of your shelf-confidenshe... You bet!

SDP

...got a little post lined up have you ?? Shomewhere they need an arrogant, incompetent, pompoush populisht parashite?!!??

Mmm, yah — that's about right

TOUGH + TENDER BARBECUE NITE

© Steve Bell '90

..For me personally I believe it's a toss up between Archbishop of Canterbury and Manager of England

BARBECUE NITE

Panel 1: I'M GOING TO THE **EXECUTIVE TOILET** AND I MAY BE GONE RATHER A **LONG TIME**...

Panel 2: Y'KNOW — ALL YOU PEOPLE EVER BRING ME IS PROBLEMS, **PROBLEMS, PROBLEMS**...

© Steve Bell 1990

Panel 3: ONLY **DAVID, LORD SUIT,** BRINGS ME **SOLUTIONS**!

Panel 4: THIS ONE IS TWO PARTS **BULLSHIT** TO ONE PART **SLIME** TO ONE PART **TAPWATER;** THAT ONE IS ONE PART **BULLSHIT** TO ONE PART **SALIVA** TO ONE PART **JEYES FLUID**.....

MICK AND **BORIS** ARE TAKING TIME OFF AT THE **WORLD CUP**

WE'RE SICK AS **PARROTSKI**!!

COME ON YOU **CAMEROO-HOOONS**!!

ANOTHER DISASTER!

21·6·2432

HEY BORIS — YOU'RE A BUSY KIND OF A GUY — HOW DO YOU LIKE TO **RELAX** OF AN EVENING?

GIVE ME A **STRAIGHT PISS-UP** EVERY TIME.... ...FACE DOWN IN SNOW-DRIFT..... NOTHING FEELS LIKE BACARDI.... YEAH.......

...RED NOSE..... BLIND... ...STEAMING. ...FISHED OUT OF RIVER...... LET'S FACE IT I'M A **PARTYMAN** TO THE **ROOTS OF MY BOOTS**!!!

© Steve Bell '90

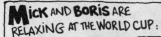

MICK AND **BORIS** ARE RELAXING AT THE WORLD CUP:

BIG LIMOS, FREE WORLD CUP TICKETS – THESE KIND OF PARTY PRIVILEGES ARE WHAT GET UP ORDINARY **SOVIET PUNTERS' NOSES!!**

MIND YOU – THEY'RE THE **ONLY REASON** I STAY IN THE PARTY, MIKHAIL......

LISTEN – EVERYBODY NEEDS A **HOLIDAY** ONCE IN A WHILE...

© Steve Bell 1990

BESIDES, I'LL TELL YOU SOMETHING THAT GETS UP ORDINARY SOVIET PUNTERS' NOSE **EVEN MORE** THAN LIMOUSINES AND FREE TICKETS......

...IT'S THIS CRIMINAL **WASTING OF TOILET PAPER** YOU INDULGE IN....

WHAT A LOAD OF **RUBBISH!!**

YOU'VE **BLOWN IT**, MIKHAIL ...TRIPLING BREAD PRICES WAS A **DUMB MOVE**.....

BOLLOCKS

YOU GOT TO BE **RADICAL**, BUT YOU GOT TO STAY **POPULAR**... ...TRIPLING BREAD PRICE IS **NOWHERE**.....YIS NOT **RADICAL**......

YOU GOT TO MULTIPLY PRICES BY **TEN** OR **TWENTY** TIMES – – KEEP THE FOCKERS **REELING** – DON'T LET THEM REGAIN THEIR BALANCE.... ...BE LIKE **MARGARET** – – BE TOUGH.... BE LIKE **IRON BASTARD!!!**

BUT WHAT ABOUT SUFFERING MASSES?

LET THEM EAT **PIZZA!!**

© Steve Bell '90

15

16

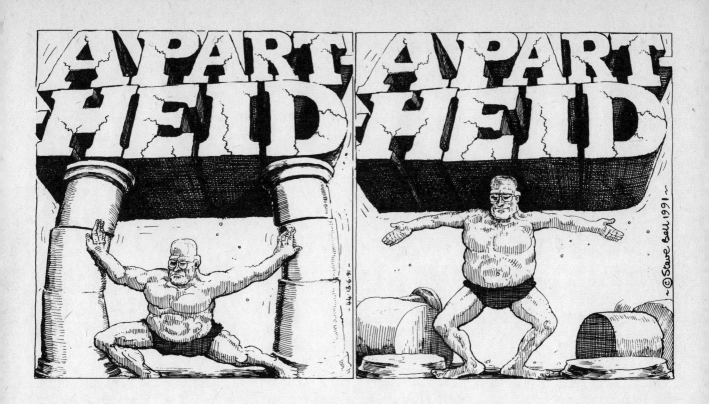

JULY

© Steve Bell 1990

© Steve Bell 1990

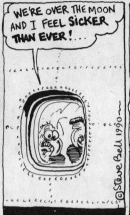

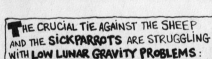

- 2·7·2441 -

THIS IS THE **CRUCIAL AREA**, LADS

YOUR AIM MUST BE TO GET POSSESSION, GET TO HERE, AND THEN GET INTO WHAT I CALL "**FART IN A TRANCE**" MODE. ANY QUESTIONS??

@Steve Bell '90

WHAT ARE YOU TALKING ABOUT?

WELL SON, IT'S PARTLY A **SPIRITUAL THING** – WHICH BRINGS ME TO PHASE **TWO** OF MY PLAN.....

I WANT YOU ALL TO **TURN CATHOLIC**. I'VE BOOKED THE **HOLY FATHER** FOR TONIGHT......

TEL – WHAT'S YOUR VIEW OF THE **CATHOLIC/NON-CATHOLIC** THING? SHOULD OUR BOYS **CONVERT** – OR **NOT**?

YOU GOTTA RE-RUN THE **FIFTH PENALTY** FROM THE **IRELAND-V-RUMANIA** MATCH, BRIAN....

- 3·7·2442 -

YES, TEL, IT'S A **GREAT SAVE** BY THE PLUCKY IRISH GOALIE..

...BUT **SO WHAT**?

@Steve Bell 1990

....YOU GOT TO ADMIT – 'E DONE GOOD, **THE BOY DONE GOOD**, BRIAN

YES, YES, BUT SO **WHAT**?? AND BY THE WAY – BRIAN'S ON THE OTHER SIDE...

SO 'E **DIDN'T CROSS 'IMSELF**! ALL THE PREVIOUS **FOUR**, 'E DONE THE **BEAD TICKLER'S SALUTE** BEFORE 'AND, AND 'E **MISSED EVERY ONE**!! I REST MY CASE.

21

FATARSE THE VULTURE

HOSPITAL

YOU SILLY PEOPLE HAVE GOT COMPLETELY THE **WRONG IDEA** ABOUT ME....

...**EATING** THIS HOSPITAL FOR LUNCH IS THE **FARTHEST THING** FROM MY MIND. IT SIMPLY ISN'T ON THE AGENDA....

...**THIS KNIFE AND FORK** IS JUST A DEVICE FOR **DIVIDING** THIS INSTITUTION INTO **CONVENIENT BITE-SIZED SELF-GOVERNING UNITS !!**

THEN **HOW** DO YOU EXPLAIN THIS **SAUCE BOTTLE?**

© Steve Bell 1990

FATARSE THE VULTURE

YOU PEOPLE REALLY ARE **PATHETIC!** WHAT ON EARTH GIVES YOU THE IDEA THAT MY FRIENDS AND I WISH TO **EAT THIS HOSPITAL**....

...IT'S JUST RIDICULOUS **SCAREMONGERING!** I'VE ALREADY EXPLAINED THE **KNIFE AND FORK;** THE **SAUCE BOTTLE** IS SIMPLY TO ENHANCE THE **VIABILITY** AND **EFFICIENCY**.......

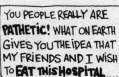

© Steve Bell 1990

...OF EACH INDIVIDUAL **BITE-SIZED SELF-GOVERNING UNIT.** I WOULD HAVE THOUGHT THAT MUCH WAS **OBVIOUS,** EVEN TO A **POLITICALLY MOTIVATED GAGGLE** OF **EMPLOYEES** LIKE YOU....

...AND DON'T YOU **BOLSHIE PATIENTS** TELL ME YOU DON'T WANT IT, BECAUSE YOU'RE GOING TO **GET IT** WHETHER YOU WANT IT OR **NOT !!**

27

THIS ISN'T **STRONG** ENOUGH...

DAILY Mirror
MIRROR SPORT

SCARGILL ATE MY BABY
NUM Boss in Secret
Satan Sex Ring Shocker

I WANT HIS BONES GROUND INTO **DUST**. I WANT HIM **UTTERLY DESTROYED**....

Sumptuous suite where scheming sordid Scargill bathed in the blood of babes

...I WANT HIM **PULPED PURÉED** AND **PULVERISED**... ...I WANT HIM **EXTINGUISHED** AND **EXPUNGED** FROM THE RECORD....

...IT'S THE ONLY WAY TO DEAL WITH **MEGALOMANIA** ON **THAT SCALE**.!!

DANGER **HAZARD TO SHIPPING**

WODGER RECKON, COL—I MEAN — IS SCARGILL **GUILTY** OR IS HE **GUILTY**??

JUST LET ME GET MY HANDS ON THE BASTARD, I'D.....

...I'D DUST ORFF THE OL' **BLACK CAP**, PLONK IT ON WITH A FLOURISH...... ...AND YOU KNOW WHAT I'D DO THEN??

WHAT?

WHAT?

I'D LAUNCH INTO THE "I SENTENCE YOU TO BE TAKEN FROM HERE TO A PLACE OF EXECUTION"...ROUTINE AND YOU KNOW WHAT — I'D DO IT WITH A BLOODY GREAT **SMIRK** ACROSS MY FACE.!!

FWORRGH! **NICE ONE!!**

KNOCK OUT

HEY — HERE'S **JOHN** WITH THE **ROLLS**! WHAT'S UP JOHN —YOU GOT A **FACE** LIKE A **DOG'S ARSE**??? WE'RE HAVIN' A GREAT LAUGH HERE — **CHEER UP** YOU OL' **STIFF!!**

HAM
SPAM
SMOKED SALMON

AUGUST

The NHS Reforms and You

The National Health Service and Community Care Act 1990 will bring about important changes in the way our caring services are run. There have also been changes in the way the family doctor service operates. Others are planned for dental care. These changes, and those arising from the Act, are designed to give you a more efficient and an even better service – above all, a service that puts you, the patient, first.

They are intended to reinforce the main aim of the National Health Service – to help people live longer and enjoy a better quality of life. As a matter of fact, today's NHS, employing record numbers of doctors and nurses, is treating more people than ever before.

As now, the NHS will continue to be open to all, regardless of income, and paid for mainly out of general taxation. NHS services will continue to be largely free at the point of use.........

The NHS Reforms and You

A word of reassurance

Changes in health services affect everyone. Some people are worried about what services will be available. Some of the questions being asked are:

- will my doctor be able to spend as much time with me?

- will I continue to get my prescriptions, even if the medicines are expensive?

- if my family doctor has a practice fund, will I still get the treatment I need?

- can I still have treatment at a local hospital?

- will I still have a choice about where I have my baby?

- will hospitals which become self-governing NHS Trusts stay completely within the NHS?

So, quite simply, the answer to all these questions is "You must be joking"

What services should you now look out for?

For all adults

- Regular 'life-style' check-ups will be available. These will be offered to you when you first register with a doctor or if you have not seen your doctor for some time. The purpose of these check-ups is to:

  - give you the chance to discuss anything worrying you;

  - provide an opportunity to carry out a few simple tests (such as checking your blood pressure);

  - offer professional advice if needed on such matters as diet, exercise, smoking and alcohol consumption.

In other words, your GP can advise you on how to look after yourself. This may include recommending that you attend one of the practice's health promotion clinics.

The NHS Reforms and You

A new way of running NHS hospitals and units – NHS Trusts

What is an NHS Trust?

- Hospitals and other health service units which become NHS Trusts will remain firmly part of the NHS but they will be run by their own boards of directors, rather than the local health authority. They will have a range of powers and freedoms not available to other units. These will include the ability to own their assets, employ their own staff and set their rates of pay, and borrow money to develop their services.

- NHS Trusts will allow local management and staff with firsthand knowledge of the needs of local people and patients to have more control over their own work and the running of their hospital or unit. The point of this is to enable them to improve standards and the quality of care available to patients.

- Hospitals and health service units will **only** be allowed to become NHS Trusts when they are judged to be ready to make the best use of the freedom of NHS Trust status to benefit NHS patients.

- The first hospitals will become NHS Trusts in April 1991. Before an NHS Trust is established, all those with an interest – staff, GPs, health authorities, community health councils and above all, the local public – will be asked their views about an application to set up a Trust and will have an opportunity to express an opinion. These views will be taken into account when a decision is made on the application should they concur with those of the Secretary of State.

Will NHS Trusts have control over services they provide?

- Yes, but where a service must be provided locally an NHS Trust can be obliged to provide it if it is the only hospital able to do so. This will ensure the continued provision of essential local services.

Are hospitals which become NHS Trusts going to remain completely within the NHS?

- Yes. They will continue to be run by NHS staff on NHS property, providing NHS services to NHS patients.......

The NHS Reforms and You

The NHS Reforms and You

How will your choice of where to go for treatment be affected by the new arrangements?

■ Your needs and wishes and the preferences of your GP will be taken into account by your local health authority when making agreements with hospitals on the services to be provided. Health authorities will do this by asking local people what they think of the services on offer and by discussion with local GPs.

■ You and your GP will be involved in making the decision about where you go for treatment. The choice should be greater because your local health authority will not be restricted to making agreements on services with hospitals within its own boundaries. It will be able to make agreements with other hospitals if better quality or quicker treatment can be obtained there.

Choosing where to go for treatment

■ Your doctor will be aware of the range of hospitals offering services, and will be able to recommend to you the hospital where you will receive the best and most appropriate care. Each health authority will retain some money to pay for referrals by GPs to hospitals which are not covered by existing agreements on services.

© Steve Bell 1990.

THE HEALTH SERVICE

The NHS Reforms and You

As now, the NHS will continue to be open to all, regardless of income, and paid for mainly out of general taxation. NHS services will continue to be largely free at the point of use.........

Donor Card

BARCLAYCARD VISA

WELCOME

I DON'T LIKE THE OLD-STYLE "CHURCH OF ENGLAND" IMAGE... ...WE NEED A NEW STYLE EFFICIENT BUSINESS ORIENTATION....

...THE VERY WORD "CHURCH" IS TOO **BUILDINGY**, IT'S NOT NINETIES.... WE NEED.... A NEW CONCEPT...... .....LET US PRAY, GUMMER... ...PERHAPS THE LORD WILL SPEAK TO US....

© Steve Bell 1990

KLANNG

NYAHAAH!!

JEEZGEN plc!! QUICK! GET ME **TWO** MERCHANT BANKERS PRONTO!

YES.... **JEEZGEN** plc ©™ CAN BE **YOURS** FOR AS LITTLE AS....WELL, YOU **NAME** YOUR PRICE!!...

© Steve Bell 1990

WE'RE TALKING **MEGA-JUMBO** ASSET PROFILES HERE!! THERE'S A **JEEZGEN** © SOUL CENTRE IN VIRTUALLY **EVERY** TOWN AND VILLAGE IN THE COUNTRY!

TELL YOU WHAT — YOU PUT AN **OFFER** ON THE TABLE, I'LL MAKE IT WORTH YOUR WHILE. HOW DOES **3 MILLION QUID** FOR THE MOSQUE MINI BUS FUND SOUND ??

LET ME GET THIS STRAIGHT — I PUT, SAY **50 PEE** ON THE TABLE YOU GIVE ME **3 MILLION QUID** FOR KEEPING IT ON THE TABLE ...THEN IF SOMEBODY ELSE COMES ALONG WITH A **BETTER BID**, I KEEP THE 50 PEE **AND** THE THREE MILLION QUID. IS THAT **ABOUT RIGHT?**

THAT'S IT IN A NUTSHELL!

HERE'S 50 PEE

AHH....YES....COME IN...
...SIT DOWN....

-1977-8-8-

IT HAS COME TO MY ATTENTION THAT YOU...ER... ERRM...HOW SHALL I PUT IT... ....HRRRUMMPH....YOU ARE... ERRMMM...YOU HAVE BEEN.... ...ER...HRRRUMMPHH

YOU'VE HEARD THAT **I** AM A **PRACTISING PULPIT POOF**. AM I RIGHT??

THERE'S REALLY **NO NEED** FOR US TO DESCEND TO THAT SORT OF **CHEAP TABLOID LANGUAGE**!

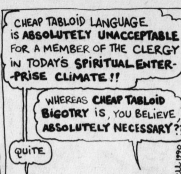

CHEAP TABLOID LANGUAGE IS **ABSOLUTELY UNACCEPTABLE** FOR A MEMBER OF THE CLERGY IN TODAY'S **SPIRITUAL ENTER- PRISE CLIMATE!!**

WHEREAS **CHEAP TABLOID BIGOTRY** IS, YOU BELIEVE **ABSOLUTELY NECESSARY??**

QUITE

© Steve Bell 1990

COME!

OH!...ER...I'M SORRY TO DISTURB YOU, ARCHBISHOP ELECT, BUT MIGHT I HAVE A **WORD**?

9·8·2468

ERRM...IT'S ABOUT SOMETHING RATHER **SENSITIVE**...... ...PERHAPS THESE GENTLEMEN...??

OH, DON'T MIND **THEM**....

— © Steve Bell 1990 —

...THEY ARE **TWO** INDEPENDENT MERCHANT BANKERS WHO ARE HERE TO ADVISE ME ON THE PROPRIETY OF THE **JEEZGEN** plc ©™- SALE ...

...ONLY PROPER MERCHANT BANKERS HAVE THE DEGREE OF **SKILLED DETACHMENT** NECESSARY TO JUDGE THESE MATTERS TRULY **OBJECTIVELY**!

WHAT ARE THE WHEELBARROWS FOR??

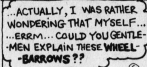

...ACTUALLY, I WAS RATHER WONDERING THAT MYSELF... ...ERRM... COULD YOU GENTLEMEN EXPLAIN THESE WHEELBARROWS??

10·8·2469

I MEAN, DO THEY HAVE SOME KIND OF ARCANE CEREMONIAL FUNCTION FOR MERCHANT BANKERS?

AHRRRMM

— © Steve Bell 1990 —

OH I SEE— —IT'S A FORM OF COLLECTION TRAY WHEREIN YOU ACCEPT TOKEN GRATUITIES...

...LIKE THE VICARS' PENSION FUND.... ......CRIKEY!!

WELL THIS IS EXCELLENT! WE'VE HAD AN OFFER FROM LORD HANSON!! HE IS PREPARED TO TAKE JEEZGEN© OFF OUR HANDS!

HMMM   HMMM

11·8·2470

...HE SUGGESTS ONE OR TWO STRUCTURAL ALTERATIONS WHEREBY WE DIVIDE THE ERSTWHILE C. of E. INTO TWO FUNCTIONING UNITS...

QUITE   QUITE

'NATIONAL SALVATION' plc™ WILL ENCOMPASS THE ENTIRE CLERGY, ADMINISTRATORS, PASTORAL COMMITMENTS, CASSOCK IMPORTS etc. etc.... AND 'JEEZGEN' plc, WHICH WILL ENCOMPASS ALL THE REAL ESTATE AND THE FIXTURES AND FITTINGS....

INDEED   INDEED

© Steve Bell 1990

...HE IS PREPARED TO MAKE AN OFFER FOR 'JEEZGEN' plc© ™. RIGHT NOW, PROVIDING WE PAY HIM AN UNDERWRITING FEE OF 12 MILLION POUNDS. DOES THAT SOUND REASONABLY ABOVE BOARD TO YOU MERCHANT BANKERS??

PERFECTLY   PERFECTLY

MONSIEUR L'ARTISTE HAS SECURED A JOB AS **OFFICIAL WAR ARTIST** WITH THE **MORNING MULE**, BUT IS BORED ALREADY....

THE BOSS WANTS ONE OF SADDAM EATIN' A BRITISH AIRMAN BY FIVE O'CLOCK!

MMMMMM.....YOU NEED TO WORK UP THE **FANGS** A BIT....

PAH!! ZE INDIGNITY!! ZIS IS **NURT** ZE RÔLE I ENVISAGED FOR UN VRAI **ARTISTE DE LA GUERRE**.... ...I NEED TO BE URN ZE SPURT WIZ ZE ÉLITE **SHURCKFARCE**....

DAMN THIS SWELTERING FOG!!

BELGIANS AHOY, SAH!!

STARK BOLLOCK NAKED UP THE **GULF** IN A **GAS MASK**! AM I GOING MAD OR IS HISTORY REPEATING ITSELF, ABLE SEAMAN??

THERE'S A 'COPTER APPROACHING CAPTAIN!

IS IT FRIENDLY?

I DON'T KNOW — I HAVEN'T TRIED STROKING IT YET, SAH!...

DID WE ORDER THREE HUNDRED WORLD WAR TWO **GREATCOATS** AND ONE OFFICIAL **WAR ARTIST**, ABLE SEAMAN??

I THINK IT MAY BE ANOTHER **BALLS-UP**, CAPTAIN!

CAN YOU 'URLD ZAT POSE FOR JUSTE FAHVE MINUTES?

© Steve Bell 1990

40

SEPTEMBER

3.9.2477

'URLD ZAT POSE AND SAY "FROMAGE" MATELOT

☉✿☉!!!

AHH, ZIS CREZZY WURRR — ONE MINUTE: STARK BOLLOQUE NEKKED, ZE NEXT MINUTE: SEALED URP IN PLOSTIQUE BARGS!!

NO BROKEN BOTTLES

MERDE! ZESE SUITS REDUCE MA OPERATIONAL EFFECTIVENESS BY 80 POUR CENT...

UNIDENTIFIED OBJECT APPROACHING!!

OH MY GOD!! IT'S ONE OF THE VERY LATEST INTELLIGENT 'SMOKEFISH' MINES, AS INNOCENTLY SOLD TO SOME PASSING IRAQIS A COUPLE OF MONTHS OR SO AGO!!

I'M COMING TO GET YOOU!!

© Steve Bell 1990

OH NO! OH NO!! THE HIGHLY INTELLIGENT "SMOKEFISH" MINE IS THE ULTIMATE IN DESTRUCTIVE NAVAL TECHNOLOGY!! TAKE EVASIVE ACTION!!!

I'M COMING TO GET YOOOU!!!

4.9.2478

IT HAS THE UNCANNY ABILITY TO IGNORE ALL DIVERSIONARY TACTICS AND ENGAGE IN PSYCHOLOGICAL WARFARE AT THE SAME TIME!!

I'M COMING TO GET YOU!!

THERE IS NO KNOWN MEANS OF AVOIDING THIS LITTLE SWINE! I THINK WE COULD BE DONE FOR, CAPTAIN!!.. CAPTAIN?? WHERE'S HE GONE??

I'M COMING TO GET YOU!!

© Steve Bell 1990

...UNLESS.... OF COURSE!! WE MUST APPEAL TO IT'S SENSE OF VANITY! QUICK!! WAR ARTIST!!!

WOULD YOU LARK YOUR PURTRAIT PANTED IN OILS??

WEE-E-E-ELL!!!

43

MONSIEUR WAR ARTISTE HAS SAVED THE CREW OF H.M.S. TEASMADE BY OFFERING TO PAINT THE PORTRAIT OF AN ULTRA-INTELLIGENT BUT HOSTILE MINE......

CAN YOU 'URLD ZAT POSE??

HURRY UP... I'M A BUSY MINE!

PSSST!! TAKE YOUR TIME, MONSIEUR!

DID YOU KNOW I WAS BORN NEAR ALDERSHOT AND I'VE BEEN A MEMBER OF 'MENSA' SINCE I WAS SIX MONTHS OLD...

FASCINATING... ...FASCINATING

© Steve Bell 1990

'MENSA'?...WHAT IS ZIS 'MENSA'??

IT'S ACTUALLY AN ORGANISATION FOR THE EXTREMELY INTELLIGENT!...

..AHHHH....YOU MEAN ZAT BURNCH OF OUANQUÈRES 'OO LARK DOING PURZZLES?...

I BEG YOUR PARDON???

OH NO!!

FOR GOD'S SAKE, MONSIEUR WAR-ARTISTE — DON'T UPSET THE INTELLIGENT "SMOKEFISH" MINE — IT'LL BLOW US ALL SKY HIGH!!

MEMBERSHIP OF 'MENSA' IS NOT OPEN TO ANY OLD MINE, Y'KNOW...

PAH!

LISTEN TO MOI, YOU SILLY LEEDLE BURX OF TREECKS.... ...IF YOU 'AVE TO JOIN STUPIDE URGANISATIONS LARK 'MENSA' — ZAT IN ITSELF IS AN ADMISSION OF CHRONIQUE INADEQUACY!!

I BEG YOUR PARDON?!

© Steve Bell 90

YOU ARE A BURNCH OF OUANQUÈRES!! AH REST MA CASE!!

NO! NO-OO!!!

RIGHT!! THAT'S IT!!! YOU'VE HAD YOUR CHANCE!

PLEASE! PLEASE!! IGNORE MONSIEUR L'ARTISTE — IT'S ARTISTIC TEMPERAMENT — IT MEANS NOTHING!! PLEASE DON'T BLOW US UP! HE HAS AN IMMENSE TALENT! — YOU MUST EXCUSE HIS RUDENESS!!

EITHERE YOU WISH TO BE IMMURTALISED, OR GO POUFFE!! SEE IF I CARE!!

44

50

OCTOBER

55

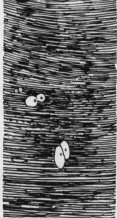

60

Panel 1: IRON SPEARHEAD TO IRON LADY: ARE YOU RECEIVING ME?? **OVER**.

CRACKLE...LOUD AND CLEAR. WHAT DO YOU **WANT**? OVER... ZZZZZTT...

Panel 2: ...WE NEED **MONEY**, IRON LADY — I'VE JUST BEEN LOOKING AT THIS **CATALOGUE** I BORROWED OFF A PASSING BEDOUIN........

Panel 3: ...WE NEED 200 TITANIUM-TOOLED BARRELS AND A GOOD SUPPLY OF G48 'RIDICULOUS' MISSILES.... ...THAT COULD COME TO... ...LET ME SEE...WITH DISCOUNT...LESS V.A.T. BECAUSE IT'S TECHNICALLY FOR EXPORT...

Panel 4: ...WE'RE ONLY TALKING AN EXTRA **£1 MILLION A DAY** OVER **75 YEARS** ..... IT'S NOT CHEAP, BUT THEN, IF YOU WANT US TO DO THE JOB **EFFECTIVELY**...

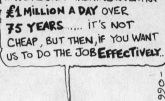

© Steve Bell 1990

Panel 5: ...I SEE.....YES.....MMM... ...I QUITE UNDERSTAND, IRON LADY. IT'LL BE DIFFICULT, BUT : "**NEEDS MUST WHEN THE DEVIL DRIVES**" WHAT? OVER...

Panel 6: STAND EASY, CHAPS — I'VE JUST BEEN IN COMMUNIC-ATION WITH THE **IRON LADY** AND SHE'S AGREED TO OUR **EQUIPMENT** NEEDS....

© Steve Bell 1990

Panel 7: ...THERE IS JUST ONE **SMALL SNAG** HERE : IN ORDER TO PAY FOR 200 NEW TITANIUM-TOOLED BARRELS EQUIPPED WITH G48 'RIDICULOUS' MISSILES, WE ARE ACT-UALLY GOING TO HAVE TO MAKE A **SMALL ADJUST-MENT** TO YOUR PAY AND CONDITIONS....

Panel 8: ...LET ME PUT IT TO YOU THIS WAY : PENSIONS AND LIVING QUARTERS ARE AN INCREASINGLY **OLD-FASHIONED CONCEPT** IN THIS NEW **AGE OF ENTERPRISE**....

...SO A SMALL CUT IN YOUR EMOLUMENTS **NOW** TO PAY FOR NEW BARRELS COULD BRING **UNTOLD BENEFITS** IN YEARS TO COME....

12·10·2511

HI·FIBRE LO·FAT LAGER

Blitzbrau

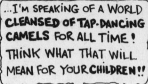

...I'M SPEAKING OF A WORLD **CLEANSED** OF TAP-DANCING CAMELS FOR ALL TIME! THINK WHAT THAT WILL MEAN FOR YOUR **CHILDREN**!!

ANY QUESTIONS??... ...THAT MAN **THYAH**...??

WHAT IF WE SAY 'NO'??

Blitzbrau LITE LAGER

© Steve Bell 1990

THEN YOU'LL BE INSIDE THE **GLASS HOUSE** BEFORE YOU CAN SAY "BARRACK ROOM BOLSHIE..." **GOOD GOD!!** YOU'RE A **WOMAN!!!**

Blitzbrau HI·FIBRE LO·FAT

I'M NOT A WOMAN — —I'M A **PENGUIN**, AND I SAY: **STOP THIS NONSENSE NOW!!**

WHAT?!?! WHAT!?!?

13·10·2512

RIP

Blitzbra

GENOCIDAL HARDWARE **OUT OF THE GULF!!! NEGOTIATE** AN END TO THIS **DANGEROUS FARCE!** ARMS CONVERSION **NOW!!** INCREASE **PENSIONS!** INCREASE **CHILD BENEFIT!!!** ABOLISH **TRIDENT!!** EXPAND **PUBLIC TRANSPORT!!!**

YOU'RE ON A CHARGE!!

YOU CAN'T PUT ME ON A CHARGE —I'M NOT IN THE ARMY — I'M A **CAMP FOLLOWER!**

Bl

— © Steve Bell 1990 —

...AND ANYWAY: I'M **PREGNANT!**

Blitzbrau ON DRAUG...

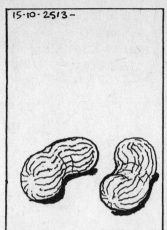

15·10·2513—

EXCUSE ME, BUT DON'T I RECOGNISE YOU FROM SOMEWHERE?

I'M SORRY, I DON'T THINK WE'VE MET

YOU'RE MICKEY THE MONKEY NUT AREN'T YOU? I'VE SEEN YOU ON T.V.!

WHY YES ACTUALLY I AM!

YOU REALLY CRACK ME UP!!

© Steve Bell 1990—

MICKEY THE MONKEY NUT! THIS IS AMAZING! YOU'RE MICKEY THE MONKEY NUT!! I LOVE YOUR STUFF!

WHY THANKYOU

16·10·2514—

I LOVED THAT ONE ON THE TELLY... ...YOU KNOW....

WHICH ONE?

YOU KNOW — THE ONE WHERE YOU WERE LYING AROUND IN A BOWL.

OH, RIGHT

WHERE DO YOU GET YOUR IDEAS FROM?

© Steve Bell 1990—

NOVEMBER

19·10·2517

JOHN! ARE YOU THERE? ARE YOU OK??

WHAP

...STOP! STOP HITTING ME WITH A STIFF WET FISH!! I'M OK...... I THINK....

...I JUST REMEMBER LISTENING TO A SUCCESSION OF TORY BULLSHITTERS, THEN A BLUR, THEN NOTHING.....

IT'S ALRIGHT —YOU'RE AMONG FRIENDS NOW, JOHN!

SKRIT   SKRAT

SO HOW ARE YOU ALL THEN?

FINE...GOT A BIT OF A SORE FLIPPER.... LIBRARY BOOKS ARE OVERDUE.... PRUDENCE IS BEING HELD BY THE BRITISH ARMY......

19·10·2518

WHAT DO YOU MEAN "PRUDENCE IS BEING HELD BY THE BRITISH ARMY"??

AACH...I WASH MY HANDS OF THE SILLY GIRL!!!

WE'VE HAD A POSTCARD, LOOK!

"SOMEWHERE IN THE GULF, MID TO LATE 1990-ISH DEAR MUM, I'VE BANGED UP IN A BRITISH ARMY GLASS HOUSE IN CENSORED. YOU'LL NEVER GUESS, BUT VINCE AND I ARE DELIGHTED TO ANNOUNCE THAT I'M EXPECTING A CENSORED THAT IS, OF COURSE IF WE ALL SURVIVE THIS CENSORED LUNACY. YOUR LOVING DAUGHTER, PRUDENCE "

WHAT ARE YOU GOING TO DO?

I DON'T KNOW — I THOUGHT YOU MIGHT BE ABLE TO THINK OF SOMETHING

WHAT DO YOU THINK IT IS SHE'S EXPECTING?

MONEY? A FOOD PARCEL? WHO KNOWS??

DON'T WORRY ABOUT A THING — AFTER LAST WEEK IT JUST SO HAPPENS THAT GROCER HEATH AND ME ARE JUST LIKE THAT....... ...KNOW WHAT I MEAN? — —I'LL SORT IT OUT!!!

©Steve Bell '90

67

GROCER! HOW'S BUSINESS?

22·10·2519

WO! GIMME SOME SKIN!

YOW! JOHN! GIMME FIVE!

GIMME SOME SHOULDERS! GIMME SOME TEETH!!

HO HO HO!!! YOU SLAY ME, MY LITTLE HAIRY FRIEND!!

I DON'T WANT TO SLAY YOU—BUT I KNOW SOMEBODY WHO DOES!!

DON'T EVEN REFER OBLIQUELY TO THAT WOMAN IN MY PRESENCE!

GROCER—I HAVE A LITTLE MERCY MISSION OF MY OWN I WISH TO ACCOMPLISH..... ...BUT I CAN ONLY DO IT WITH YOUR HELP....

V.I.P. LOUNGE →

23·10·2520

..SO I WANTED TO ASK IF I COULD TAG ALONG ON YOUR MERCY MISSION AS A SORT OF FREELANCE SECURITY ADVISER

THAT'S GENEROUS OF YOU—OF COURSE DEAR BOY!

WHICH PARTICULAR ASPECT OF SECURITY DID YOU WISH TO ADVISE ME ON, JOHN?

ON THE NEED NOT TO OPEN ANYTHING WHATSOEVER FROM CENTRAL OFFICE— —I'VE HAD A TIP OFF!

— © Steve Bell 1990

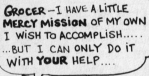

68

I THINK I'M GOING MAD! I CAN'T COPE WITH ANOTH-ER NIGHT OF RELENTLESS THROBBING....

...FROM THOSE DAMNED TAP DANCING CAMELS! YET I'M UTTERLY HELPLESS TO DO ANYTHING ABOUT THEM.....

RAKKA TAKKA TAKKA TAKKA TAKKA

...IT'S NOT THAT WE HAVEN'T HAD PROVOCATION ENOUGH. IT'S JUST THAT OUR CRAP TANKS ARE UNABLE TO HIT THEM EVEN WHEN THEY STAND STILL....

© Steve Bell 1990

...AND NOW TO CAP IT ALL THEY'VE SENT US A CONSIGNMENT OF "GROCER-SEEKING MISSILES". I DON'T UNDERSTAND THESE BLOODY BOFFINS....

...I THOUGHT GROCERIES WERE EXCLUDED FROM THE U.N. SANCTIONS. THE WHOLE THING SEEMS BLOODY ODD!!

SNORK

WELL...OURS NOT TO REASON WHY. IT SAYS HERE:" REMOVE CRAP TANK BARREL BY UNSCREWING CLOCKWISE...."

GOR BLIBEY! WHASS GOAD OD?

"..AND INSERT O.B.S.90 GSML GROCER-SEEKING MISSILE LAUNCHER INTO TANK TURRET, LOCATING RED DOT Ⓐ WITH PURPLE DOT Ⓑ ON TURRET COWLING NIPPLE, TURN-ING CLOCKWISE UNTIL CLICK IS HEARD."

NNGGHFF!

SOUNDS FAIRLY STRAIGHT-FORWARD." NEXT: SLIDE GROCER-SEEKING MISSILE ONTO GSML LAUNCHER UNTIL SPRING-LOADED HOOK IS ENGAGED. YOUR GROCER-SEEKING MISSILE IS NOW READY FOR FIRING."

NNNGGKK!

"NOW AWAIT TOP SECRET ORDER DIRECT FROM WHITEHALL."

...AND STILL THE TAP-DANCING CAMELS COME....

© Steve Bell 1990

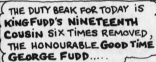

82

DECEMBER

86

87

...OF COURSE, JOHN IS VERY MUCH **HIS OWN** POODLE

THANKS TO ROGER WODDIS.

— 2·12·2555 —

— ©Steve Bell 1990 ∼

AND NOW, GENTLEMEN — — TO BUSINESS...... ITEM ONE: BREAK OUT THE **BONES** AND THE **CHOC DROPS**!! THOSE IN FAVOUR SAY '**YUP**'!

YUP! YUP! YUP! YUP! YUP!

— 4·12·2556 —

CARRIED **UNANIMOUSLY**! BONES AND CHOC-DROPS ALL ROUND PLEASE!

ITEM TWO: **WALKIES** AND **BOTTOM SNIFFING**? CARRIED **UNANIMOUSLY** THE PARTY IS **UNITED** BEHIND ME!!!

WAG SNIFF WAG WAG SNIFF

ITEM THREE: GENERAL ISSUE OF **BLUE COLLARS**!

©Steve Bell '90

88

..NOT ONLY HAS HE GOT A BLUE COLLAR — —HE FETCHES HIS OWN NEWSPAPERS!

LAWKS!

5·12·2557

© Steve Bell 1990

WELL...HAHA...THE COMMUNITY CHARGE IS SOMETHING OF A "BOMB"..

...AND MICHAEL HERE IS THE SUPREMELY EXPERIENCED BOMB DISPOSAL POODLE- -TICIAN WHO IS GOING TO DEFUSE IT!

I, BY CONTRAST, AM THE TERRORIST NUTCASE WHO PACKED IN THE SEMTEX AND FITTED THE BOOBY TRAPS....

...AND I'VE BEEN PROMOTED TO PROPAGANDA CHIEF! BOOM BOOM!!! HA HA HA!!

6·12·2558

© Steve Bell '90

89

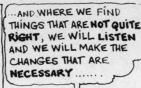

96

JANUARY

103

104

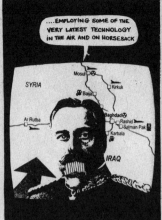

105

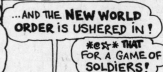

108

FEBRUARY

THERE'S NOT MUCH HOPE FOR THIS ONE,

...HE WOULDN'T SURVIVE BEING MOVED BUT HE'S STILL CONSCIOUS, SO COULD YOU SIT WITH HIM FOR A BIT...

O.K.

STONE THE CROWS!

WHO'S THAT?

IS THAT YOU, KIPLING, OR AM I SEEING THINGS??

YOU'RE NOT SEEING THINGS. I AM KIPLING

GOOD LORD! I THOUGHT YOU'D BEEN DISCHARGED FROM THE SERVICE!!

SO DID I, CAPTAIN!! UNFORTUNATELY THEY STILL KEPT MY NAME ON THE RESERVE!

BUT....BUT..... I THOUGHT YOU'D.... .....OH GOD!......

IT'S A LONG STORY, CAPTAIN MIDDLETAR...

PLEASE.....KIPLING, TELL ME......I'VE NOTHING ELSE ON AT THE MOMENT....

© Steve Bell 1991

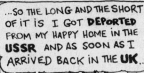

...SO THE LONG AND THE SHORT OF IT IS I GOT **DEPORTED** FROM MY HAPPY HOME IN THE **USSR** AND AS SOON AS I ARRIVED BACK IN THE **UK**...

- 6·2·2597 -

..I GOT SERVED WITH MY **CALL-UP PAPERS.** FORTUNATELY I'D DONE A COURSE INJECTING ORANGES AND BANDAGING LIFE SIZED MANNEQUINS BACK IN **1979**....

...AND THUS I CAME TO BE AN ORDERLY JUST ASSIGNED TO THIS **HOSPITAL SHIP**, AND SO WE MEET AGAIN....... .....**FUNNY OLD WORLD**, CAPTAIN MIDDLETAR....

FUNNY OLD WORLD INDEED, KIPLING. I......I.........

WHAT IS IT YOU WANT TO SAY, CAPTAIN? IF IT'S DIFFICULT TO SPEAK JUST **WHISPER** IN MY EAR

I...I...MUST CONFESS THAT I'M NOT **OVERLY THRILLED** TO SEE YOU AFTER ALL THESE YEARS, ABLE SEAMAN....

I SUPPOSE WE NEVER REALLY **GOT ON**, DID WE CAPTAIN MIDDLETAR?

YOU WERE JUST A **BLOODY BOLSHIE**, KIPLING! **STILL ARE** BY THE SOUND OF IT.....

7·2·2598

IT'S **UNFORTUNATE** THAT WE SHOULD MEET IN SUCH CIRCUMSTANCES

I'D SAY IT'S UNFORTUNATE THAT WE SHOULD HAVE TO MEET **AT ALL!**

© Steve Bell 1991

I'D BETTER LET YOU **REST**, CAPTAIN

NO...**NO!** I DON'T **WANT** TO REST, KIPLING.. ......I DON'T THINK I'D WAKE UP AGAIN IF I SLEPT NOW.......

I WANT TO **DRINK** A **G. & T.**, SMOKE A **PIPE** AND **CURSE** THIS **BLOODY STUPID** WAR WHILE I STILL HAVE BREATH LEFT IN ME.....

NO HEROICS THEN, CAPTAIN?

ABSOLUTELY NONE! PASS ME MY PIPE!!

119

MARCH

123

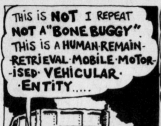

STILL NO WORD!

zzzSNORK... WHAT??

STILL NO WORD FROM **PRUDENCE** OR **JOHN**...

DON'T WORRY GLORIA—SHE'LL BE ALL RIGHT— SHE'S GOT THE **LUCK OF THE PENGUINS**!

© Steve Bell 1991

DID I EVER TELL YOU ABOUT THE WAY I MIRACULOUSLY SURVIVED **THIRTEEN MISSILE ATTACKS** AND SUSTAINED **ALBATROSS BOMBARDMENT** IN THE **FALKLANDS**?..... ...**UUURRGHH**!!! ME **WAR WOUND**!!!

WAR WOUND??? YOU NEVER MENTIONED ANY **WAR WOUND** BEFORE?

IT'S AN OLD **STOMACH WOUND** I GOT DURING A PARTICULARLY **FEROCIOUS LUNCH** BACK IN '82!

OF COURSE I'M WORRIED —THEY WERE HURLING AROUND MORE HIGH EXPLOSIVES THAN IN THE **WHOLE** OF **WORLD WAR TWO**, AND SHE WAS IN THE **MIDDLE** OF IT. I'D BE MAD **NOT** TO BE WORRIED!!

KNOCK KNOCK

12·3·2620

© Steve Bell '91

HELLO?

ARE YOU **GLORIA PENGUIN**?

YES?

I'VE HAD A **LETTER** FROM MY **SON VINCENT** IN THE **GULF**....

OH REALLY? PLEASE COME IN

HE SAYS HE'S **DESERTED THE COLOURS** AND IT'S ALL BECAUSE OF **YOUR DAUGHTER**!

I BEG YOUR **PARDON**?

I JUST WANTED TO SAY HOW **GRATEFUL** I WAS TO HER!

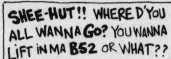

129

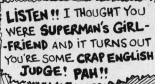

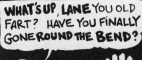

APRIL

THEY'LL ALL JUST HAVE TO WAIT AND SEE, IF I MAY SAY SO.... ..WAIT AND SEE....

OH YES....ALL IN THE REMARKABLE FULLNESS OF TIME....I HAVE THE ANSWERS, OH YES.....

— 27·3·2633 —

I KNOW THE ANSWERS BUT THEY WILL HAVE TO WAIT AND SEE...... I HAVE THE ANSWERS...

THEY'RE LOCKED SAFELY IN MY POUFFE AND ONLY I HAVE THE KEY!!

28·3·2634 —

OH GOLLY!! SOMEBODY'S BROKEN INTO THE POUFFE AND STOLEN MY SECRET PLANS!!!

© Steve Bell '91

NORMA?? HAVE YOU SEEN MY SECRET PLANS ANYWHERE ?!

THEY WERE IN THE POUFFE WITH MY 'O' LEVEL CERTIFICATES!! NORMA?? NORMA??

THE BOYS FROM THE GREY STUFF

WELL, CLARKE, WHAT EXACTLY DOES THIS **Standard ATTAINMENT TEST** INVOLVE??

FIRSTLY, I JUST WANT YOU TO **RELAX** AND ACT **NATURALLY**...

...DON'T BE **INTIMIDATED** BY ANYTHING ABOUT THIS **TEST**...IT DOESN'T INVOLVE **PASSING** OR **FAILING**....

IT SIMPLY INVOLVES ME CLASSIFYING YOU AS EITHER ① A **DOLT** ② **AVERAGE** OR ③ A **SMARTARSE** ALL YOU HAVE TO DO IS READ THIS PASSAGE ALOUD...

The boy stood on the burning deck Whence all but he had fled....

IF YOU HAPPEN TO MAKE A **MISTAKE**, DON'T BE ALARMED IF I MAKE A LOUD **FARTING NOISE**... ...ON YOUR MARKS, GET **SET**... **GO!!**

The boy stood on the burning deck Whence all but he had Fled....

THE BOYS FROM THE GREY STUFF sit their S.A.T.s

...THIS IS **EASY**, I KNOW THIS ONE.... "THE BOY STOOD ON THE BURNING DECK ONCE ALL BUT HE HAD... **THRRRRARRP!!**

The boy stood on the burning deck Whence all but had fled.

DON'T WORRY, MAJOR MINOR, THAT'S JUST THE **BLUNDER ALARM**...IT DOESN'T CONCERN YOU AT ALL....

BLUNDER? I MADE NO **BLUNDER!**

YOU SAID "**ONCE**" - YOU SHOULD HAVE SAID "**WHENCE**"

...NOW I SIMPLY WRITE DOWN THE WORD YOU SUBSTITUTED IN THE **SCIENTIFIC BOX** PROVIDED. IF YOU'D MISSED IT OUT ALTOGETHER I WOULD HAVE BLOWN A **WHISTLE**, AND IF YOU'D ATTEMPTED IT BUT FAILED I WOULD HAVE PULLED THIS **CHAIN**....

IS THAT **ALL CLEAR** TO YOU NOW?

UMMMMM...

QUAACK!!

THAT'S FOR **HESITATION**

WELL CLARKE — AFTER ALL THAT — HOW DID I DO IN MY S.A.T.??

I'VE COLLATED ALL YOUR RESULTS USING A **TOP SECRET SCIENTIFIC FORMULA** KNOWN ONLY TO **MYSELF**, AND YOU'LL BE PLEASED TO HEAR I'VE GOT A **RESULT**

...BUT FIRST LET ME EXPLAIN THE CLASSIFICATIONS: **LEVEL ONE** DOESN'T MEAN YOU'RE A FAILURE, IT JUST MEANS THAT YOU HAVE ACHIEVED **DOODLY SQUAT**; LEVEL **TWO** MEANS **AVERAGE**; AND LEVEL **THREE** DOESN'T MEAN YOU'RE A **SUCCESS**, IT JUST MEANS YOU'RE **GRAMMAR SCHOOL MATERIAL**

JOHN — I'M PLEASED TO TELL YOU THAT YOU'VE ATTAINED **LEVEL TWO!**

YOU MEAN — I'M **AVERAGE??** **YIPPEE!** DO I GET A **CERTIFICATE??**

NO, MAJOR MINOR — YOU DON'T ACTUALLY GET A **CERT-IFICATE** FOR BEING **AVERAGE**

OH WHY **NOT??** THAT'S NOT **FAIR!** I'M EXCEP-TIONALLY **AVERAGE** FOR MY AGE AND HEIGHT!?...

...I FEEL THAT DESERVES SOME SORT OF **RECOGNITION**

OH ALL RIGHT — I TELL YOU WHAT — I'LL KNOCK YOU UP SOMETHING; I AM **SECRETARY OF STATE FOR EDUCATION** AFTER ALL!

THANK YOU CLARKE — AT LAST I HAVE **AUTHENTIC PROOF** THAT I HAVE A **MIND!**

This is to Certify that MR AVERAGE has achieved an average level of attainment as scientifically determined by the whim of the Secretary of State for Education

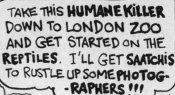

TUT TUT — LOOK AT THESE POOR VICTIMS OF HIGH-SPENDING LABOUR CAMDEN : TWO TO A CAGE WITH A COMMUNITY CHARGE OF SEVERAL HUNDRED POUNDS!

REGENT'S PARK ZOO

-19·4·2647-

I'M JUST GOING TO PUT THEM OUT OF THEIR MISERY

UNDER OUR NEW **LOCAL TAX** WHICH I'M NOT AT LIBERTY TO REVEAL THE **DETAILS** OF YET, YOU'LL BE AT LEAST ONE HUNDRED AND NINETY TWO POUNDS AND FORTY * PENCE BETTER OFF!!

CHEESE!

©Steve Bell '91

* THE FIRST NUMBER THAT CAME INTO MY HEAD PLUS 17½%

LABOUR COUNCILS **DAMAGE YOUR WEALTH** ..... WHY ARE YOU **SPITTING** AT ME??

HELLO .... THIS IS A PARTY POLITICAL **PHOTO OPPORTUNITY** ON BEHALF OF THE CONSERVATIVE PARTY

-20·4·2648-

... I'D LIKE TO ASK YOU **HOW MUCH** YOU THINK THE AVERAGE **LABOUR COUNCILLOR** COSTS YOU MORE THAN A CONSERVATIVE?

I'LL TELL YOU: **TWO HUNDRED AND ONE THOUSAND FOUR HUNDRED AND SIXTY** POUNDS AND THIRTY EIGHT PEE..!!

©Steve Bell '91

LET'S FACE IT — YOU'D BE **BETTER OFF DEAD** THAN HAVING TO LIVE UNDER A **LABOUR** AWWK!

MAY

THIS IS **RATTY PRATT IN THE AFTERNOON** AND I'M TALKING TO PRIME MINISTER **JOHN MAJOR** HERE ON ONE....

OOH MY HEAD!!

HOW **LONG** HAVE YOU BEEN SLAM DANCING THEN, PRIME MINISTER?

WELL, FRANKLY I'M A BIT OF A **NOVICE**....

...THE CHAPS AT IMAGE CONTROL SAID: "**BE COOL JOHNNY, BE COOL!**" SO I THOUGHT I'D MAKE MYSELF MORE **INTERESTING** TO THE **YOUNGER TYPE** OF PERSONAGE....

...ACTUALLY I DON'T LIKE **LOUD UNPLEASANT MUSIC** AT ALL... ...I LIKE **LIGHT MUSIC** TO A MODERATE EXTENT.... ...I ALSO QUITE LIKE THE **HUM** YOU GET FROM CERTAIN FORMS OF **ELECTRICAL HOUSEHOLD APPLIANCE**.......

WHICH PERSONS **THIS CENTURY** DO YOU MOST ADMIRE??

RUPERT BEAR AND MARGARET THATCHER

I ADMIRE RUPERT BEAR FOR HIS **POLITICAL PHILOSOPHY**, AND I ADMIRE MARGARET THATCHER FOR **GIVING ME A JOB**

WHAT'S YOUR IDEA OF **PERFECT HAPPINESS**?

HAVING A SHAG UP A TREE WHILE LISTENING TO '**CATS**' BY ANDREW LLOYD WEBBER !

YEAH!

AND HOW WOULD YOU LIKE TO BE **REMEMBERED**??

BY A FAIRLY ENORMOUS **CONCRETE GNOME** IN PARLIAMENT SQUARE!

I CAN ASSURE YOU ALL **NOW**, WHOLEHEARTEDLY AND CATEGORICALLY, AS MY PULLOVER LIVES AND BREATHES, THAT **EVERYTHING THAT IS BEING DONE FOR THE UNEMPLOYED IS BEING DONE**...

MMM

...AND WHENCE HERE FURTHERTOFORE WHOMSOEVER AMONG YOU NEEDS **HELP** SHALL ALMOST PROBABLY RECEIVE HELP **WITHIN A FEW NUMBER OF WEEKS**.....

MMM

© Steve Bell 1991

...SAVE IN THOSE **PARTICULAR INSTANCES** WHERE THE INDIVIDUAL CONCERNED HAS **QUIT** HIS OR HER EMPLOYMENT **VOLUNTARILY**, FOR NO MATTER WHAT REASON, IN WHICH CASE...

MMM

MMM

MMMM

...BENEFIT SHALL **NOT BE PAYABLE** UNTIL AN INTERVAL OF **TWENTY SIX WEEKS** HAS ELAPSED, UNLESS THE CLAIMANT SHOULD **PREDECEASE HIS OR HER CLAIM**, IN WHICH CIRCUMSTANCE.....

MMM!

WHAT A NICE, STRAIGHTFORWARD, **LIKE-ABLE GUY!**

WHAT'S NEXT ON MY BUSY SCHEDULE? "**VISIT THE SICK** (GULF PULLOVER OPTIONAL)"

2·5·2658

© Steve Bell 1991

← Financial Therapy

← Walletoscopy

← Cashology

← Affordectomy

HELLO SIR! ARE YOU GETTING **VALUE FOR MONEY?**

I... I DON'T HAVE TO **PAY** DO I??

DON'T WORRY — **TRUST ME — I'M IN BANKING**, AND THIS IS A METAL DETECTOR!

152

PEEEEOPLE.... ♪ PEOPLE WHO NEED PO-OPES...

...ARE THE MUCKIEST PEOPLE ♫ IN THE WORRLD....

IAN - I'M WORRIED...

WHAT ARE YOU WORRIED ABOYT, JIM??

NOBODY'S TURNED UP TO OUR SPECIAL PROTESTANT TALKS ABOYT TALKS ON ROCKALL YET!

DON'T WORRY JIM.... ...SOMEONE'S BOYND TO TURN UP SOONER OR LATER. WE MUST NOT YIELD TO THE SIREN VOICES OF PETTY-MINDED NOSHNALISTS!!

GURK!

GURK?

DENIS! THESE PEOPLE THINK I'M WONDERFUL!!

WE'RE SO HEPPY YOU CAME ALL THIS WAY, MA'AM!!

WHITE IFRICA WELCOMES THE FORMER IRON LADY

WE'D BE DIPLY DIPLY HONOURED IF YOU WOULD KISS OUR HIPPOPOTAMUS!

DELIGHTED TO! SMACK! SMACK!

CONSERVATI' ABROAD

WE'D BE THRILLED TO BITS IF YOU'D OPEN THIS NEW FULLY-INTEGRATED CROWD CONTROL EQUIPMENT FECTORY FOR US, MA'AM!

CHARMED I'M SURE!

I SNIP

..IT BRINGS A TEAR TO MY EYE .. TO FEEL THE WARMTH OF YOUR RESPONSE AFTER ALL THESE MONTHS IN THE POLITICAL WILDERNESS! THANKYOU FOR MAKING ME FEEL NORMAL AGAIN!!

OOPS! I MUST STOP THIS TIRRIBLE WHITE ON WHITE VIOLENCE!

I KLANG

WE ARE A GRANDFATHER, OH YES! WE ARE A GRANDFATHER!

GRANDAD! GRANDAD!!

DANDLE DANDLE

GRANDAD! WHAT DID YOU DO DURING THE GULF WAR?

ME? I WATCHED TELEVISION AND I'M PROUD OF IT!!!

GRANDAD! GRANDAD!! WHAT'S A "HAS-BEEN"?

HOW DARE YOU, CHILD!! I'LL HAVE YOU KNOW I'M STILL A MAJOR PLAYER ON THE WORLD STAGE!!

...WHY, ONLY YESTERDAY IN THE CITY, I INSTIGATED MOVES TO BUY UP HOUSE OF WINDSOR®™

FLIP

COO! BOGGLE BOGGLE!! THERE'S BEEN A DAWN RAID ON 'HOUSE OF WINDSOR®™ BY TURD TRUST plc!!

IT'S AN OFFSHORE BLIND BARKING TRUST BASED ON ROCKALL. LORD TURD® HIMSELF HAS ISSUED A STATEMENT....

SHOULD I AUTO-DEFENESTRATE YET??

HE SAYS, AND I QUOTE: "LARGE CONCENTRATIONS OF HEREDITARY WEALTH COULD BE BETTER MANAGED SO GIVE ME A SLICE OF THAT CIVIL LISTACTION OR I'LL LIE ON THE CARPET AND SCREAM!"

YES, YES, BUT HOW IS HE GOING TO FUND THE BID??

WHO IS THIS LORD TURD?

HE CLAIMS TO BE HEREDITARY OWNER OF A MULTI-BILLION POUND WAR-CHEST AND GUANO MOUNTAIN!

GOOD LORD! THIS IS ITE·RAGEOUS!! LISTEN TO THIS...

"DEAR QUEEN, JUST A LINE TO LET YOU KNOW THAT YOU ARE THE SUBJECT OF A HOSTILE TAKE-OVER BID, YOURS SINCERELY, LORD TURDSON"

UNSPEAKABLE ITE·RAGE!! WHO IS THIS LORD TURDSON? CERTAINLY NOT ONE OF MINE!! THIS IS FRIGHTFUL!! ...AND LOOK, THERE'S MORE...

"...P.S: YOUR DOGS MUST DIE"

NOW THAT CERTAINLY IS HOSTILE!!

© Steve Bell '91

WHAT ARE WE GOING TO DO ABITE THIS HOSTILE TAKEOVER BID, OLD GEL??

I THINK WE'LL HAVE TO "MOUNT A DEFENCE" AS THEY SAY IN THE CITY...

WHAT DOES THAT MEAN?

I'M NOT SURE - I THINK IT MEANS WE START SECKING EVERYBODY....

....AND INCREASING OUR OWN SALARIES BY AT LEAST DOUBLE THE RATE OF INFLATION.... ...I THINK THET'S HIGH THEY DO IT IN THE CITY!!

HOUSE OF WINDSOR BUSINESS PLAN

WHAT ABITE THE DOGS?

WE PROMOTE THEM TO THE BOARD!

RRRRR

© Steve Bell 1991

157

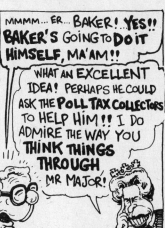